The Trauma Reaction Workbook

For kids

By Beth Richey, LCSW, RPT-S

Illustrated by Mary Lurvey

For Drew, who supports me through all my projects.

The Trauma Reaction Workbook

For Kids

Table of Contents

A Note About This Workbook

The Trauma Reaction Workbook for Children is a therapeutic resource filled with creative and engaging activities which help address children's unique post-trauma reactions.

The over 40 interventions use a variety of drawing and writing prompts, problem solving activities, visualization, and coping skills identification to help address the root of each reaction. The interventions aim to increase self-awareness and understanding while decreasing the severity of post-trauma symptoms.

This workbook is designed ONLY for qualified professionals as a part of a broader trauma treatment approach. It was written with children ages 6-12 in mind. Many of the exercises, however, can be used with all ages or in groups.

Trauma reactions to stressful events vary from child to child. This workbook allows you to tailor the appropriate interventions to each client's individual PTSD symptoms; not all pages are clinically applicable for all youth. Use your own assessment and your clinical knowledge of the child to determine pacing, interventions, and application. Carefully incorporate gradual exposure, as appropriate, and seek clinical supervision by a licensed professional. Interventions are meant to be spaced out over time (i.e. one or two per session) after a level of therapeutic rapport has been established.

Not all children process best through writing or drawing prompts, and may benefit from less directive and more creative interventions. For children that do, this book is for them.

Introduction: How to Use This Workbook

The trauma reactions within the workbook are categorized into four main categories which correspond to the four domains of post-trauma symptoms/reactions: Behavior Reactions, Body Reactions, Brain & Thinking Reactions, and Feelings Reactions. Page numbers to the associated interventions are listed next to each trauma reaction on the checklist, however many of the interventions can be used for multiple domains.

Instructions for Using Workbook Alone:

Begin by introducing the four domains of trauma reactions during the psychoeducation portion of treatment. Help the client identify their unique trauma reactions by using the included Trauma Reaction Cards™ Checklist. Reading the checklist aloud, have the client indicate whether or not each reaction is present for them while marking down their answers. This can be completed in one session, or over several (for example focusing on one category per weekly session) if clients are highly symptomatic or trauma avoidant. This method can also be used with caregivers to help them gain an understanding of their child's unique trauma reactions with the benefit of normalizing behaviors. Assist the client in completing the "Trauma Reminders: What Triggers These Reactions?" page and reading the "You Are NORMAL! Why We Have Trauma Reactions" page. Incorporate the following appropriate interventions as clinically appropriate.

Instructions for Using Workbook with Trauma Reaction Cards™ :

Begin by describing the four domains of trauma reactions during the psychoeducation portion of treatment. Introduce each card as clinically and developmentally appropriate and help the youth go through each card per category and endorse the trauma reactions which pertain to them by placing them in a separate pile. Once all cards have been reviewed and trauma reactions identified, check off the endorsed trauma reactions on the Trauma Reaction Cards™ Checklist. This can be completed in one session, or over several (for example focusing on one category per weekly session) if clients are highly symptomatic or trauma avoidant. This method can also be used with caregivers to help them gain an understanding of their child's unique trauma reactions with the benefit of normalizing behaviors. Assist the client in completing the "Trauma Reminders: What Triggers These Reactions?" page and reading the "You Are NORMAL! Why We Have Trauma Reactions" page. Incorporate the following appropriate interventions as clinically appropriate.

Trauma Reaction Cards™ Checklist
What Are Your Trauma Reactions?

Behavior Reactions

- [ ] Acting younger than you are (pp. 34, 37, 49, 51, 54)
- [ ] Arguing (pp. 14, 15, 41)
- [ ] Avoiding people, places, things, or sensations related to the trauma (p. 20)
- [ ] Bathroom problems (pp. 29, 49, 51, 54, 55)
- [ ] Breaking things (pp. 8, 14,15, 16, 17, 37, 40)
- [ ] Crying (p. 21)
- [ ] Cursing (pp. 8, 14, 15)
- [ ] Difficulty separating from caregivers (p. 13)
- [ ] Fighting (pp. 14, 15, 16, 17, 37, 40, 41)
- [ ] Hitting (pp. 8, 14, 15, 37, 40)
- [ ] Hurting your own body (pp. 8, 12, 16, 17, 37, 40, 49, 51, 54)
- [ ] Isolating yourself from others (pp. 9, 19, 29)
- [ ] Lying (pp. 8, 18, 37, 40)
- [ ] Not listening/defiance (pp. 11, 14, 15)
- [ ] Outbursts of anger (pp. 14, 15, 16, 17, 37, 40)
- [ ] Running away (p. 8, 19, 29, 37, 40)
- [ ] School problems (p. 10)
- [ ] Stealing (p. 8, 19, 37, 40)
- [ ] Taking out your feelings on people you care about (pp. 11, 43)
- [ ] Tantrums (pp. 8. 14. 15. 42)
- [ ] Trouble getting along with others (pp. 14, 15, 22, 23, 24)
- [ ] Trouble with eating (pp. 19, 22, 49, 51, 54)
- [ ] Trusting others too quickly/ Inappropriate boundaries (pp. 23, 24, 55)
- [ ] Trying to end your life (pp. 12, 19, 29, 37, 40, 51)
- [ ] Unsafe sexual practices (pp. 37, 40, 49, 51,54, 55)
- [ ] Using drugs/alcohol (pp. 12, 16, 17, 34, 37, 40)

Body Reactions

- [ ] Being on guard or constantly alert (pp. 28, 29, 30)
- [ ] Bellyaches/Nausea (p. 27)
- [ ] Body feeling of panic (pp. 28, 30, 32, 33, 34)
- [ ] Body feeling shaky (pp. 28, 32, 33, 34)
- [ ] Body or muscles tense (pp. 28, 32, 33)
- [ ] Feeling disconnected from your body (p. 34)
- [ ] Feeling like you are re-experiencing the trauma (pp. 34, 48)
- [ ] Feeling short of breath (pp. 28, 32, 33)
- [ ] Headaches (p. 26)
- [ ] Hyperactive (pp. 28, 32, 33)
- [ ] Jumpy or easily startled (pp. 28, 32, 33)
- [ ] Low energy (p. 9)
- [ ] Nightmares (pp. 30, 31, 35)
- [ ] Trouble with eating (pp. 22, 27)
- [ ] Trouble with sleep (pp. 30, 35)

Feelings Reactions

- [ ] Angry (pp. 37,39, 41, 45)
- [ ] Ashamed (pp. 37,39,41, 42, 45)
- [ ] Betrayed (pp. 43, 45, 46)
- [ ] Depressed (pp. 37, 39, 41, 42, 44, 45)
- [ ] Easily upset (pp. 37, 39, 41, 42, 44, 45)
- [ ] Embarrassed (pp. 37, 39, 41, 42, 45)
- [ ] Feeling different from others (p. 51)
- [ ] Guilty (pp. 37, 39, 41, 42, 45)
- [ ] Having worries (pp. 37, 39, 41, 44, 45, 53)
- [ ] Helpless (pp. 9, 49, 54, 55)
- [ ] Hopeless about future (pp. 9, 39)
- [ ] Moody/Irritable (pp. 37, 39, 42, 44, 45)
- [ ] Nervous/anxious (pp. 32, 33, 37, 39, 53)
- [ ] Not enjoying the things used to (pp. 22, 51)
- [ ] Not caring about others (pp. 22, 49, 51, 54)
- [ ] Numb (pp. 22, 29, 34, 51)
- [ ] Rejected (pp. 37, 39, 41, 43)
- [ ] Sad (pp. 37, 39, 41, 42, 44, 45)

Brain & Thinking Reactions

- [ ] Blaming yourself/ "It's my fault" (pp. 50, 52)
- [ ] "Everyone is unsafe" (p. 55)
- [ ] Difficulty concentrating/focusing (pp. 30, 32)
- [ ] Forgetting parts of the trauma (p.56)
- [ ] "I am bad" (pp. 38, 49, 54, 51, 52)
- [ ] Memories/Flashbacks (p. 48)
- [ ] Not trusting others (p. 55)
- [ ] Pictures of what happened pop into your head (p. 48)
- [ ] "The world is a bad place" (pp. 38, 52, 55)
- [ ] Thinking about dying/ wanting to die (pp. 12, 16, 17, 51)
- [ ] Thinking about the trauma often (pp. 48, 51)
- [ ] Thinking nothing good will ever happen (pp. 9, 38, 52)
- [ ] Thoughts about what happened pop into you head (pp. 48, 51)
- [ ] Trying to keep feelings/thoughts of trauma out of head (p. 48)

TRAUMA REMINDERS

Now that we know what your trauma reactions are, let's explore the trauma REMINDERS. List things you see, hear, smell, taste, and sensations that remind you of the trauma.

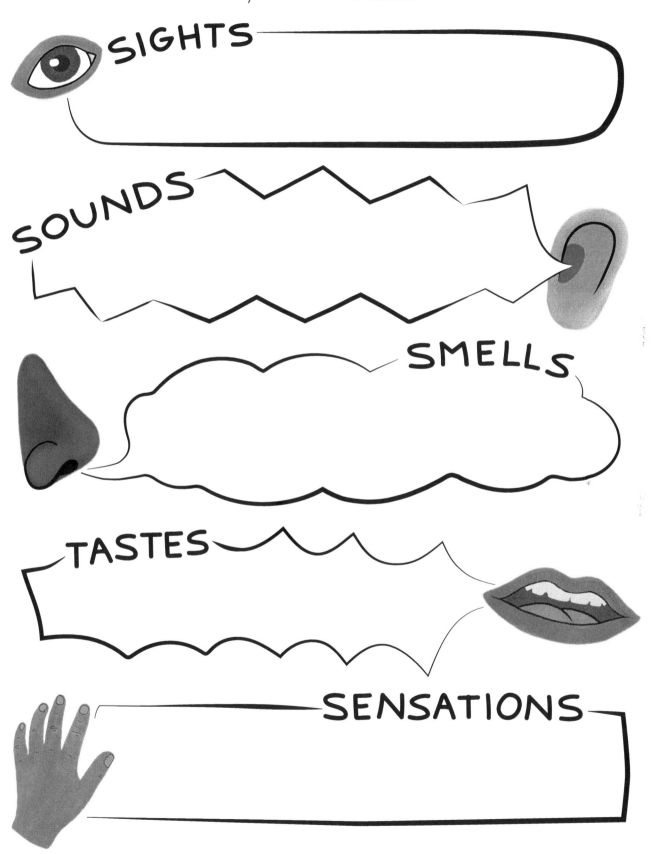

SIGHTS

SOUNDS

SMELLS

TASTES

SENSATIONS

Guess what? YOU ARE NORMAL!

The behaviors, thoughts, feelings, and sensations you are experiencing are a human's normal response to the very scary and abnormal event that happened.

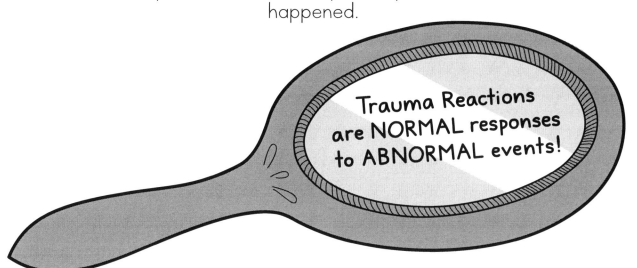

Trauma Reactions are NORMAL responses to ABNORMAL events!

I want to keep you safe, so I'm on high alert!

Why? During a traumatic experience, our brain tells our bodies to "fight, flight, or freeze" to protect us. Our brain does this by flooding our bodies with chemicals that allow us to run fast, freeze still, or fight. Your brain chooses the response most likely to help you survive.

The chemical reactions during the trauma can cause the brain to react differently in the future by going back into "fight, flight, or freeze" mode when it senses any kind of threat or reminder of the trauma. Your brain is trying to keep you safe from future danger – thank you, brain!

Sometimes, though, it's too much and interferes with living a happy life and having fun. Counseling, loving support, and talking/writing/drawing about what happened with people you trust can help.

Behavior Reactions

When we act out, it can be a message asking for help or expressing a really big feeling. Think of a time when you acted out, what help were you asking for? Fill out the letter below.

Hello.

When I _____,
I needed help and was not able to use words.
   The help I needed was
_____.

The words my body/actions were trying to say were

_____

_____.

MAKING SMALL GOALS

Fill in each step with a "mini goal" towards a positive change or future hope.
Celebrate each mini goal you achieve!

SCHOOL TROUBLES
Circle the things that make it hard at school.

WELCOME TO SCHOOL!

School work is hard
bored
too much yelling
too scared
feel rushed
feels unsafe
no friends
too many worries
can't stop thinking about the trauma
body too tense
no one likes me
can't focus
too sleepy
too hungry
I feel too mad
feel alone
can't sit still
too jumpy
it's too loud
don't care about grades
kids pick on me
mean teacher
mean school staff

sensory

academic

trauma Rx

basic needs

attention

social

FOR THERAPISTS: Clrcle the domains that the struggles fall into and use it for psychoeducational collaboration, if needed.

BEHIND THE MAD

It is common for people to take out upset feelings on someone they care about, even if, deep down, they are really mad at something else. Think of a time you took out upset feelings on someone you love. Now draw or write What or Who else you might have been upset with at the time.

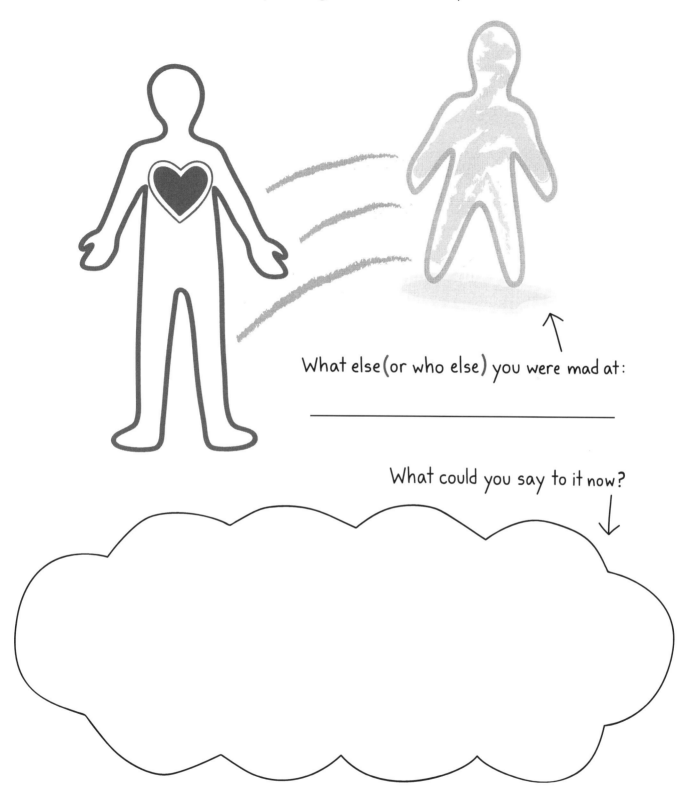

What else (or who else) you were mad at:

_____

What could you say to it now?

SAFETY PLAN

Fill out this Safety Plan with your therapist. Share it with your grown-up and keep a copy at home where you can see it. **External Triggers** are people or events in our environment that upset us. **Internal Triggers** are upsetting thoughts, feelings, or memories inside of us. Draw or write below.

My unsafe thoughts or behaviors are:

Things that trigger my unsafe
thoughts and behaviors

External Triggers

(Examples: When I see... When I hear... When someone does this...)

Internal Triggers

(Examples: When I think... When I feel... When I remember...)

I WILL USE THESE INSTEAD OF HURTING MYSELF

Support People

Write down the names of the people you will ask for help and how you will contact them.

Support Activities

Write down things you can do to feel better in the moment.

CARE COUPONS

It can be difficult to be apart from the adults that make you feel safe. Use these Care Coupons to remind each other of your connection when you are not together. You fill out one coupon and give it to the adult, and the adult fills one out to give it to you. Carry the coupon with you and look at it when it is hard to separate.

✂ one for you

- -

Dear _____,
I love you! Things I ♡ are:
_____
_____
_____

My favorite things we do together are:
_____
_____

When I miss you, I will ....

PIC OF US ☺

✂ one for me

- -

Dear _____,
I love you! Things I ♡ are:
_____
_____
_____

My favorite things we do together are:
_____
_____

When I miss you, I will ....

PIC OF US ☺

ANGRY LAVA

Sometimes, anger can start out small and get bigger and bigger until it explodes out of us like a volcano. Inside the volcano, draw or write some things that make you feel each level of lava. Next to it, write what behaviors you do when you feel a little lava, medium lava, lots of lava, and explosive lava.

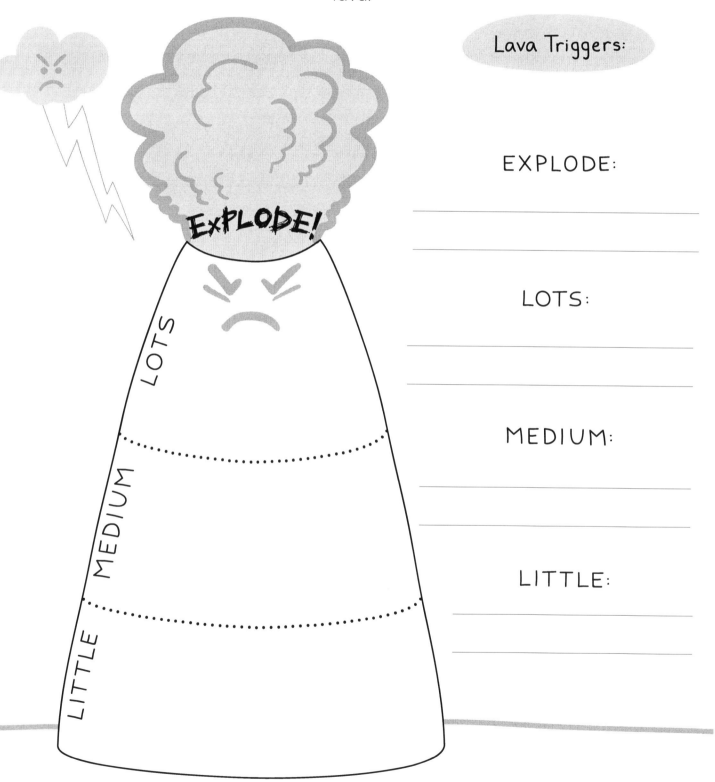

Lava Triggers:

EXPLODE:

_____

_____

LOTS:

_____

_____

MEDIUM:

_____

_____

LITTLE:

_____

_____

CALM YOUR LAVA

Lava can go back down, too, which prevents an explosion. Think of some things that help lower your anger. Draw or write the things that help lower your lava at each level.

SUPPORT ACTIVITIES

There are lots of activities we can do to help us feel better when upset. Using a support activity when upset is called using a Coping Skill. Everyone is different. What helps one child may not help the other, so it is important to identify the specific support activities that fit YOU. Circle a few that you like or are willing to try. Add your own!

call or text a supportive person

draw a picture of what is upsetting you

look up funny jokes

smell something nice

dig in dirt or sand

run

play with clay or dough

jumping jacks

take space

make a comic strip

listen to music loudly or quietly

play a video game

sing a song you like

play an online game

write someone a letter about how you feel

watch a video online

read a book

go for a walk

ask for a hug

write your feelings in a journal

do relaxing coloring pages

take deep breaths

origami

watch a show

cuddle a stuffed animal

jump rope

pet a friendly house pet

play a sport

draw

play in nature

use a fidget

knit

play tag

write a poem

do a finger labyrinth

cartwheel

pray

make a craft

paint

dance

repeat positive affirmations

Zzz...

nap

lay under a heavy blanket

listen to relaxing music

look at a calm picture

make music

do a yoga video

drink a hot or cold drink

Tips to take

1. _____

2. _____

3. _____

Write down three things to do the next time you need a coping skill. Take it with you.

UNDERNEATH A LIE
Lies usually hide a fear, worry, or secret underneath. Fill out the bubbles below.

What is something you have told a lie about?

What fear or worry was hiding in that lie?

OR

What secret was hiding in that lie?

What happened when you told the truth in the past?

What were you afraid would happen if you told the truth?

A SAFE SPACE

Draw a space that feels calm and safe. Imagine yourself here when needed.

temperature?

sounds?

real or imaginary?

smells?

colors?

inside or outside?

texture?

light?

AVOIDING REMINDERS

It's common to avoid people, places, things, and sensations related to the trauma. Make a list below of the places, people, things, and sensations that you avoid because they remind you of the trauma.

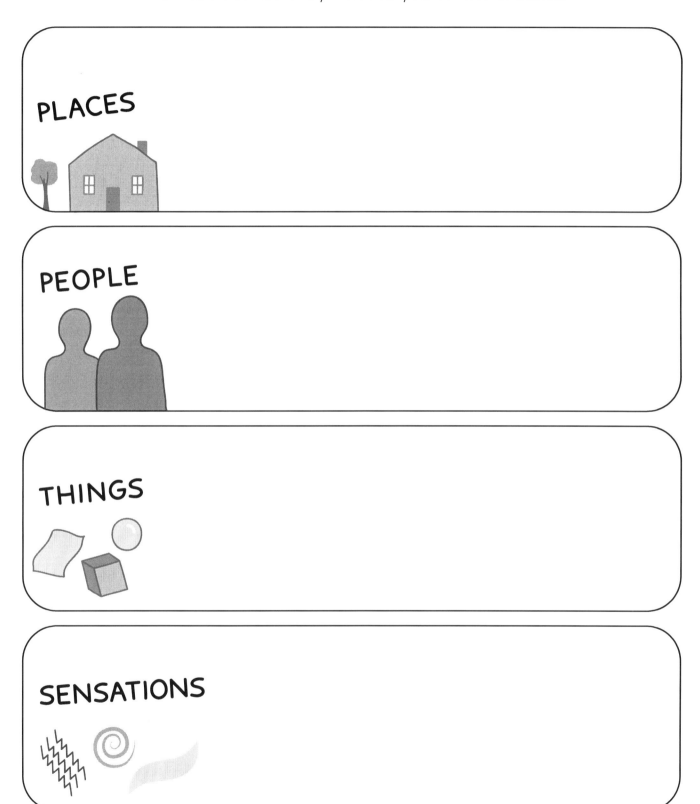

PLACES

PEOPLE

THINGS

SENSATIONS

INSIDE OUR TEARS

When we cry, there are usually a lot of feelings inside our tears that we may not be aware of. Think of some of the times you have found yourself crying, circle the other feelings that were happening. If that tear would tell you something what would it say?

FILL YOUR TANK

Pretend you have a tank that gets filled, little by little, every time you feel loved, laugh out loud, or do something that is fun and makes you happy. Draw or write in things that make you feel loved, happy, or which bring you joy.

Pretend you are out at the "Friend Store" and circle the qualities that make a safe, supportive friend. Put an X over the qualities that make for a poor friend. Come up with some of your own in the blank boxes.

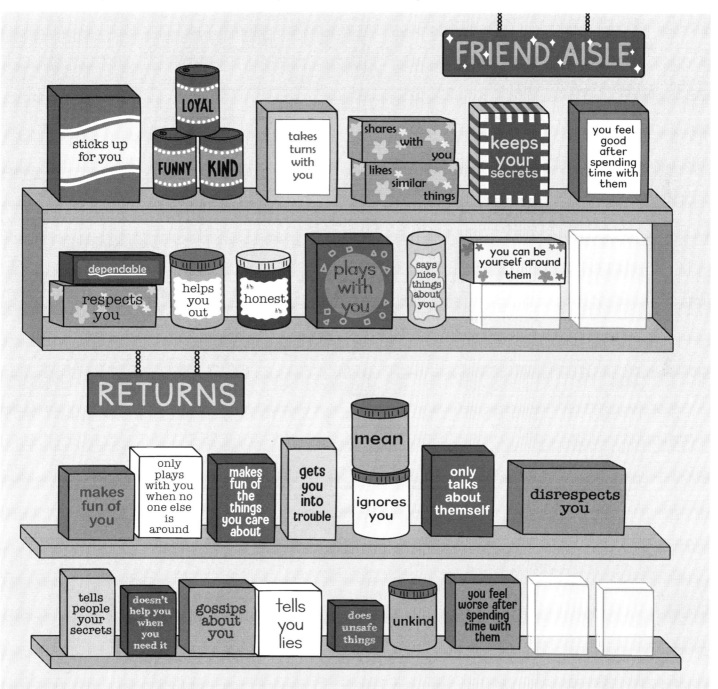

POSITIVE & SAFE

FRIENDSHIP QUALITIES

Put a check next to the positive and safe friend habits that are most important to you. Add your own at the bottom.

☐ Being kind to one another

☐ Letting each other know when they have upset you or you have upset them

☐ Waiting to tell each other personal things until you have known them a while and have built trust

☐ Helping each other

☐ Sticking up for each other

☐ Compromising on what you want

☐ Avoiding gossip about each other

☐ _____

Body Reactions

HEADACHES

Our bodies can hold things like words we want to say, memories, or feelings. If we don't let them out, they can turn into headaches or other body hurts. Draw or write below:

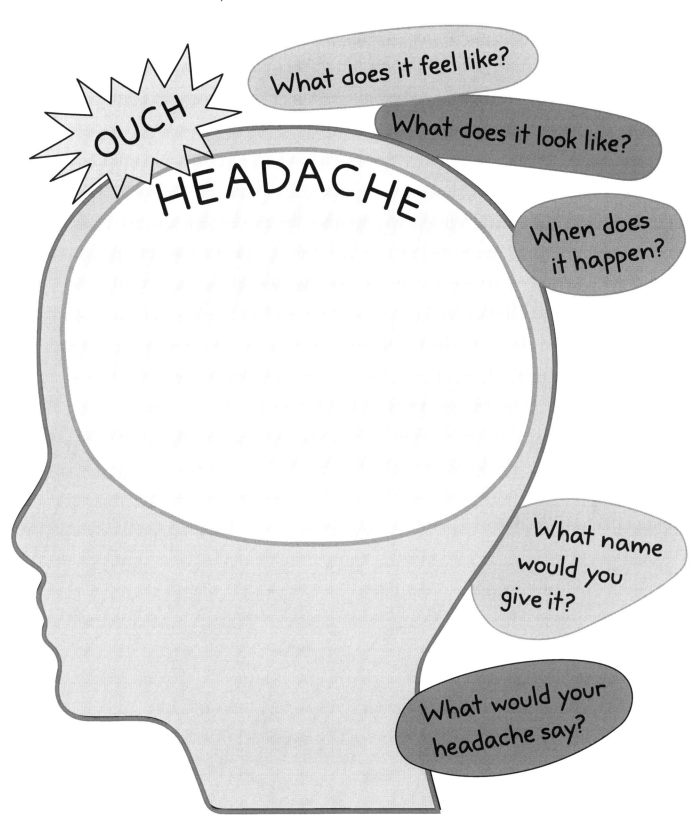

BELLYACHE/NAUSEA

Our bodies can hold things like words we want to say, memories, or feelings.
If we don't let them out, they can turn into bellyaches or other body hurts.
Draw or write below:

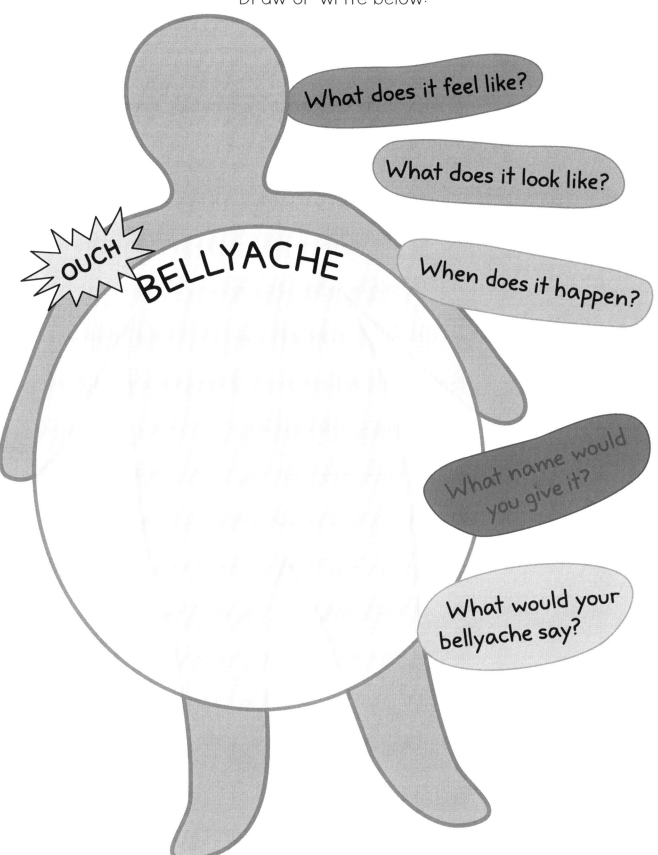

THE CALMING WAVE
Color in your calming wave any colors you like, and then practice using the below script with your imagination.

What color is your calming wave? Is it warm or cool? Does it sparkle or shine? When your body feels _____ you can use the power of your brain and imagination to calm it down and feel better! This activity can be practiced any time, with eyes open or closed, sitting or standing.

Imagine a slow, gentle wave starting at the top of your head and moving down, safely and gently calming everything it passes. It relaxes your whole face, and then soothes your neck and shoulders. The colorful wave then relaxes the area of your back and belly, then your middle and legs. The wave flows down your legs to your ankles, splashes past your toes, and goes out the bottom of your feet. Imagine, as it passes, that your special wave pushes away any upset feelings or body sensations.

WALLS OF PROTECTION

In the space below, draw protective things around the figure. What kind of protection would you like around you when you feel unsafe or scared?

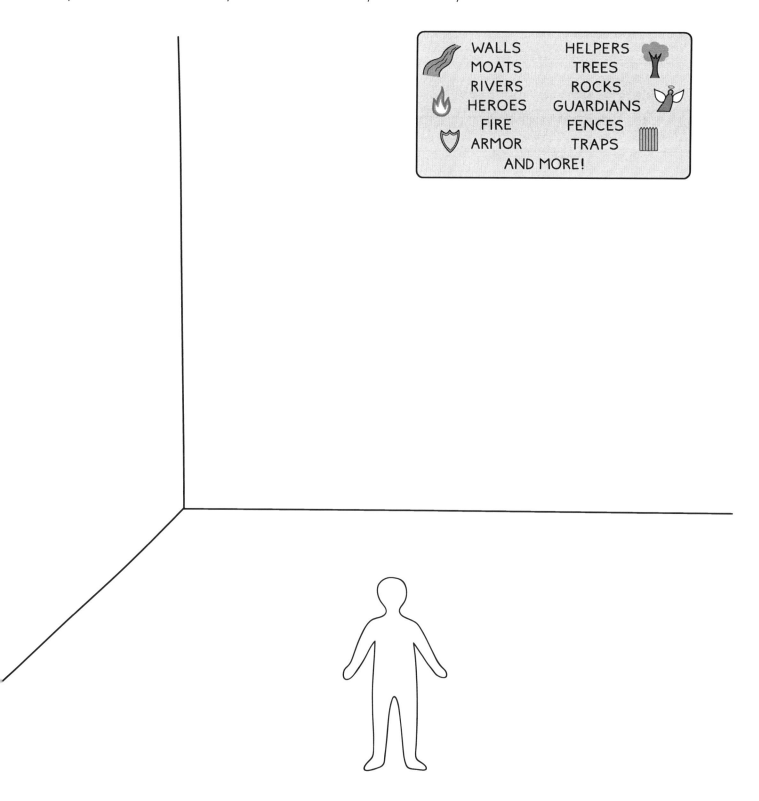

WALLS   HELPERS
MOATS   TREES
RIVERS   ROCKS
HEROES   GUARDIANS
FIRE   FENCES
ARMOR   TRAPS
AND MORE!

LEAVE IT LETTER
Sometimes we can't relax, focus, or sleep because our minds are full. Take a minute to empty your thoughts onto the paper. Try to fill up the entire page or more.

Dear Paper,

Here is a little of what is

sitting in my brain right now:

NIGHTMARES

It is common for kids who have experienced a traumatic or stressful event to have bad dreams or nightmares. Draw pictures, colors, shapes, or words that remind you of your nightmares.

Now... scribble it out!

And replace it with a safe and happy dream!

Find your Fidget

Fidgets can help focus or relax us when we have extra energy in our body. Everyone has a unique fidget fit. What helps one person may not help another. Circle the fidgets or soothing items below that would help you. Draw in your own!

soft cloth

fidget spinner

cube

sequin pillow

bouncy ball

twisty tie

button

rubber band

beaded bracelets

putty

shell

stuffie

dough

smooth stone

sand timer

finger labyrinth

bubbles

glitter bottle or liquid motion toy

spin top

hand toys

magnets

paper clip

or tap your fingers

clicky fidget

clicky pen

foam stress ball

FINGER LABYRINTH
Tracing a finger labyrinth when we are nervous, upset, or have extra energy can be calming. Try using the finger labryinth and finger path below.

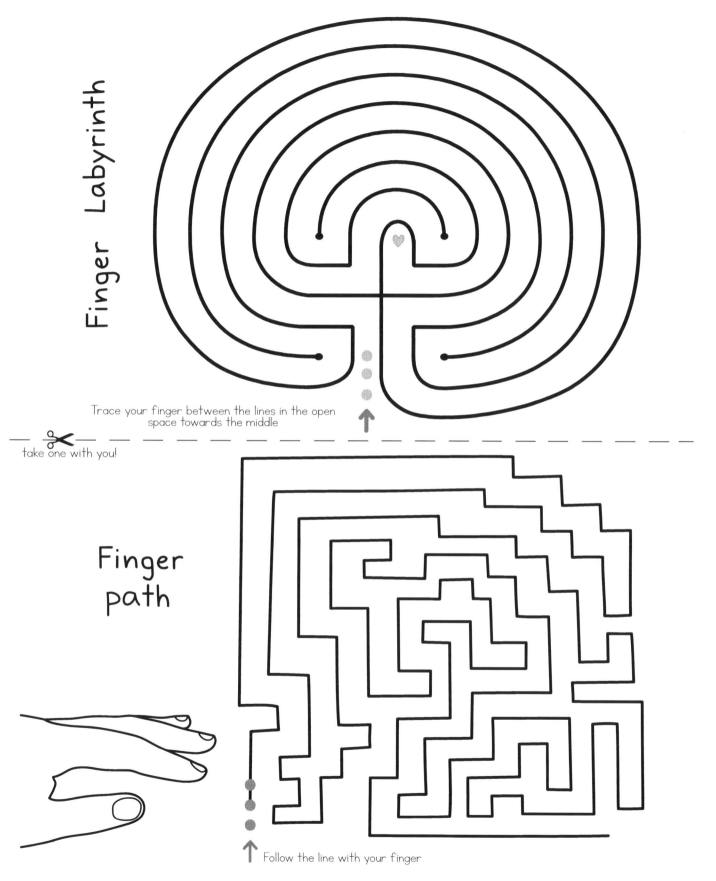

Finger Labyrinth

Trace your finger between the lines in the open space towards the middle

✂ take one with you!

Finger path

Follow the line with your finger

33

THE GROUNDING TREE

Color in your grounding tree and circle your favorite mantra at the root of the tree. When you feel disconnected from your body, practice the visualization below.

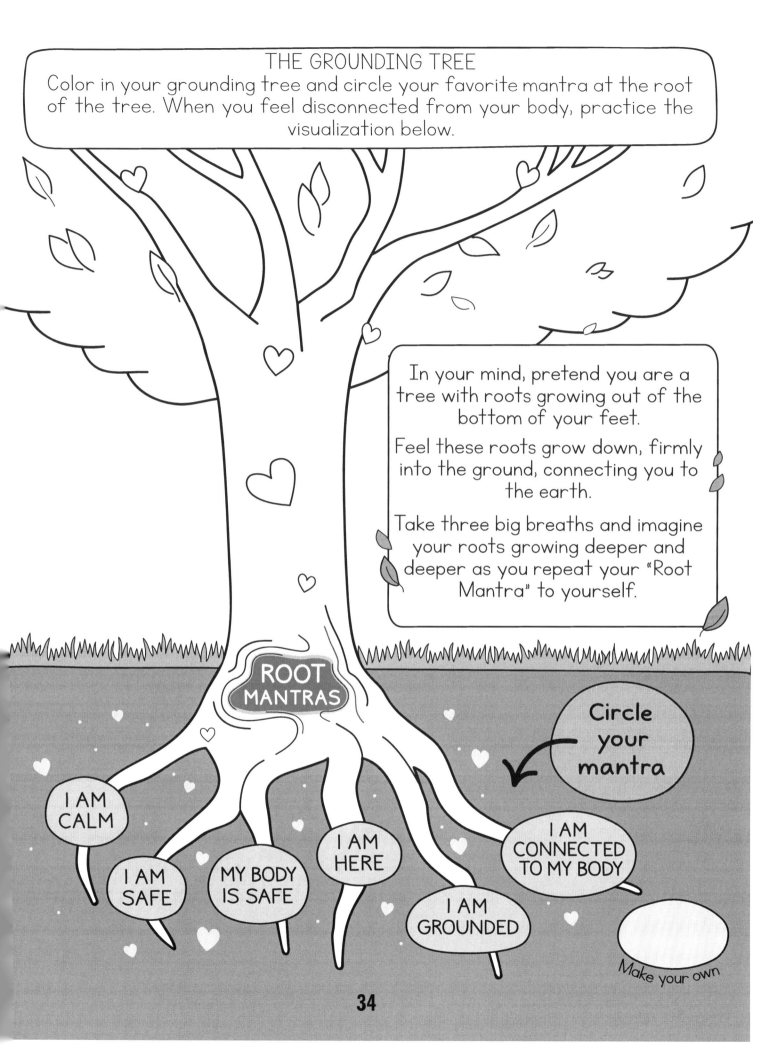

In your mind, pretend you are a tree with roots growing out of the bottom of your feet.

Feel these roots grow down, firmly into the ground, connecting you to the earth.

Take three big breaths and imagine your roots growing deeper and deeper as you repeat your "Root Mantra" to yourself.

ROOT MANTRAS

Circle your mantra

I AM CALM

I AM SAFE

MY BODY IS SAFE

I AM HERE

I AM GROUNDED

I AM CONNECTED TO MY BODY

Make your own

SLEEP SAFETY CHECKLIST

Reminding yourself of things that keep you safe can help you sleep better at night. Fill out this checklist with things that make you feel most safe. Take a copy home with you and fill it out with a grown-up before bed. Add your own ideas.

PEOPLE CLOSE BY THAT KEEP YOU SAFE

- ☐ _____
- ☐ _____

PHYSICAL THINGS TO HAVE WITH YOU

- ☐ COZY BLANKET
- ☐ GLASS OF WATER
- ☐ STUFFED ANIMAL
- ☐ HOUSE PET
- ☐ COMFY PILLOW
- ☐ _____
- ☐ _____

SAFETY CHECK

- ☐ FRONT DOOR LOCKED
- ☐ WINDOW LOCKED
- ☐ SMOKE ALARM IN THE HOUSE
- ☐ FIRE EXTINGUISHER IN THE HOUSE
- ☐ SAFETY LIGHTS/ALARM ON
- ☐ _____
- ☐ _____

ROOM THINGS

- ☐ NIGHT LIGHT
- ☐ DOOR OPEN
- ☐ DOOR CLOSED OR LOCKED
- ☐ ROOM LIGHT ON
- ☐ QUIET MUSIC PLAYING
- ☐ CURTAINS/BLINDS CLOSED
- ☐ _____
- ☐ _____

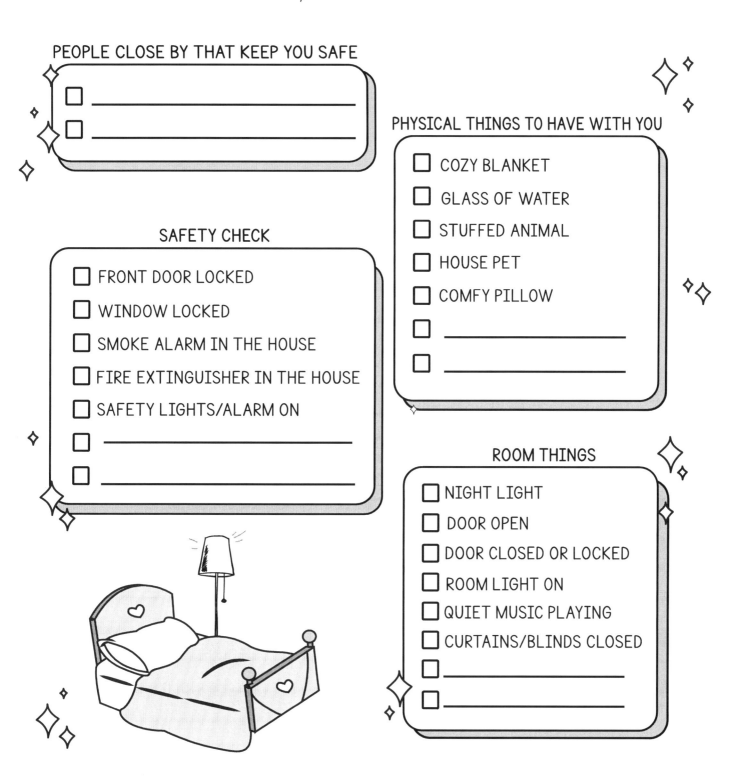

35

Feelings Reactions

THOUGHTS ARE POWER!

The things we tell ourselves in our head can cause feelings, and those feelings can trigger us to act in certain ways.

"Walking" around the cognitive triangle can help us explore what is happening inside of us. When we understand the thoughts that affect us, we can become more powerful over our feelings and behaviors!

Use the Cognitive Triangle pages to find out more.

THOUGHTS COGNITIVE TRIANGLE ACTIVITY

In the thought bubble, write or draw a time recently when you had an upsetting thought. Walk forwards around the cognitive triangle and draw or write in the heart bubble what feeling it triggered. Move forward one more time and write or draw the behavior that followed the feeling inside of the square.

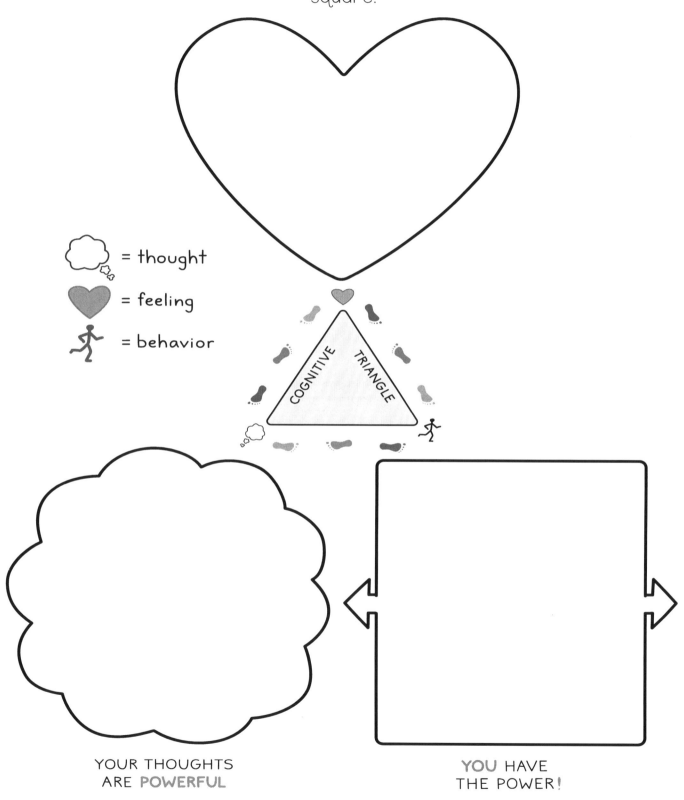

= thought

= feeling

= behavior

YOUR THOUGHTS
ARE POWERFUL

YOU HAVE
THE POWER!

FEELINGS COGNITIVE TRIANGLE ACTIVITY:

Write or draw an upsetting feeling you recently had inside of the heart bubble. Walk backwards to see what thought you were thinking that caused that feeling and draw or write it into the thought bubble. Then fast forward to after the feeling: what behavior happened? Draw or write it in the square bubble.

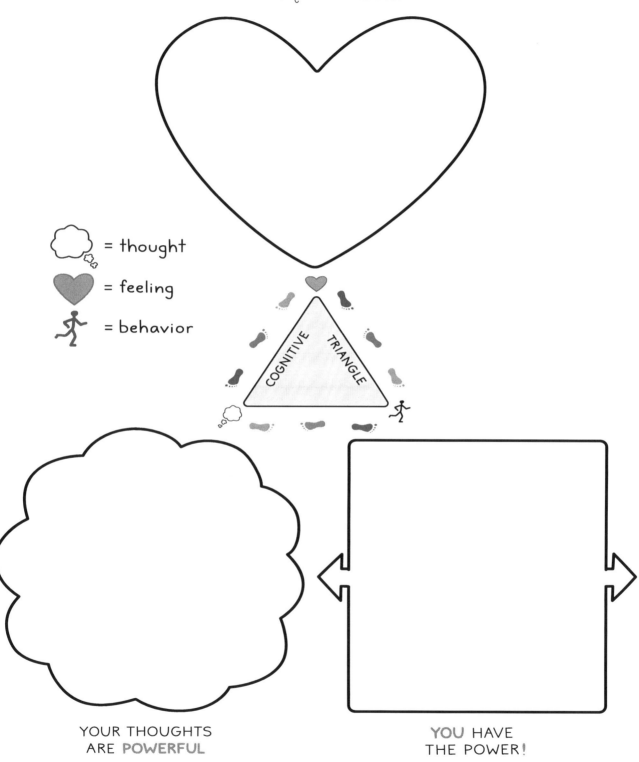

= thought

= feeling

= behavior

COGNITIVE TRIANGLE

YOUR THOUGHTS
ARE POWERFUL

YOU HAVE
THE POWER!

BEHAVIORS COGNITIVE TRIANGLE ACTIVITY:

In the square bubble, write or draw a time recently when you behaved in a way that was unsafe or unkind. Walk backwards around the triangle to the heart bubble, and draw or write what feeling came before the behavior. Then walk backwards once more to the thought bubble and draw or write what thought you were telling yourself before the feeling happened.

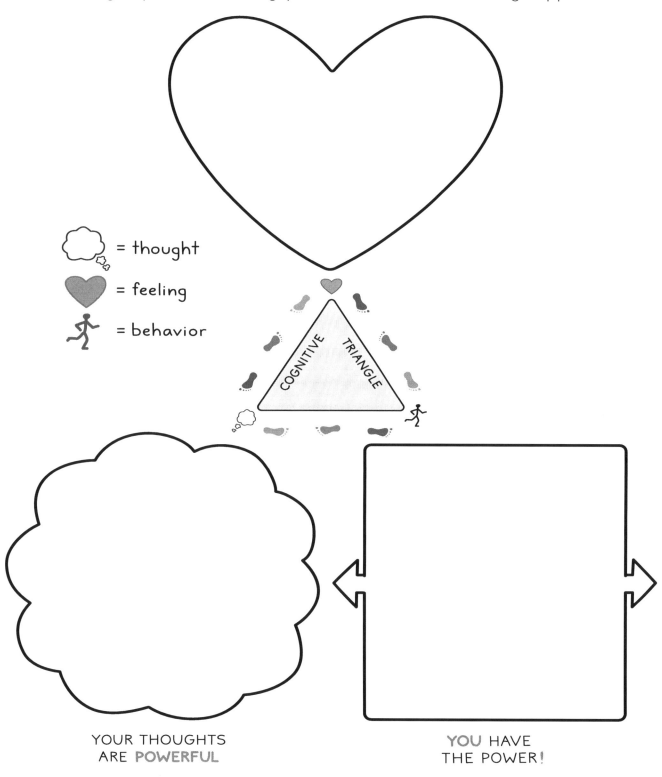

= thought

= feeling

= behavior

COGNITIVE TRIANGLE

YOUR THOUGHTS
ARE POWERFUL

YOU HAVE
THE POWER!

40

DRAW the feeling

Focus in on the feeling. Write or drawn below the characteristics it has.

feeling _____ Where does it sit in your body? _____

color _____ texture _____

smell _____ shape _____

size _____ temperature _____

Hello, feeling. I would like to say to you:

" _____

_____ "

41

FEELINGS DETECTOR

Big feelings can pop up and take over our mood (and also our behavior). Sometimes we can even get stuck in a mood. Knowing what caused a feeling can give us more power over it. The Feelings Detector first identifies the feeling, then rewinds through time to find out what event or thought triggered it. Think of a time recently when you felt yucky or upset and write or draw in the sections below.

Feeling: _____

_____

When I rewind back, I detect this is what started the feeling:

Next time you feel yucky, take out the feelings detector. First identify what the feeling is, and then rewind through time to figure out what triggered it.

42

UNSENT LETTER

Sometimes we feel betrayed, abandoned, upset, or let down by people. Sometimes these are people we care about. Sometimes they are people who have caused us harm or pain and sometimes it is both. In the space below, fill out a letter you will never send. After it is done, rip it up or keep it in your counselor's office.

I am thinking about _____ (person or situation) when I write this letter.

I am upset about _____

_____

Something I want to say to you is _____

_____

_____

I feel _____

_____

I want you to know _____

_____

Also _____

Mood Log

Keeping track of our moods helps us understand our ups and downs better. Draw or write the mood you were in each day during the morning, afternoon, and nighttime. How big was the feeling from 1 to 10? What was happening at the time?

		☀ morning	☁ afternoon	🌙 night
HAPPY	Monday	1 2 3 4 5 6 7 8 9 10	1 2 3 4 5 6 7 8 9 10	1 2 3 4 5 6 7 8 9 10	EXCITED
BORED	Tuesday	1 2 3 4 5 6 7 8 9 10	1 2 3 4 5 6 7 8 9 10	1 2 3 4 5 6 7 8 9 10	SAD
SILLY	Wednesday	1 2 3 4 5 6 7 8 9 10	1 2 3 4 5 6 7 8 9 10	1 2 3 4 5 6 7 8 9 10	LONELY
HYPER	Thursday	1 2 3 4 5 6 7 8 9 10	1 2 3 4 5 6 7 8 9 10	1 2 3 4 5 6 7 8 9 10	WORRIED
NEUTRAL	Friday	1 2 3 4 5 6 7 8 9 10	1 2 3 4 5 6 7 8 9 10	1 2 3 4 5 6 7 8 9 10	CALM
	Saturday	1 2 3 4 5 6 7 8 9 10	1 2 3 4 5 6 7 8 9 10	1 2 3 4 5 6 7 8 9 10	
	Sunday	1 2 3 4 5 6 7 8 9 10	1 2 3 4 5 6 7 8 9 10	1 2 3 4 5 6 7 8 9 10	

ANGRY   ANNOYED   SCARED   FRUSTRATED

44

FEELINGS SCALE

People have lots of feelings, and each feeling can be big, medium, or small. Below are some feelings. Take turns going through each one and sharing a time you felt that way. On a scale of 1 to 10, say how big you felt the feeling. Was it a teeny 1, or a medium 5? A high 8 or a HUGE 10?

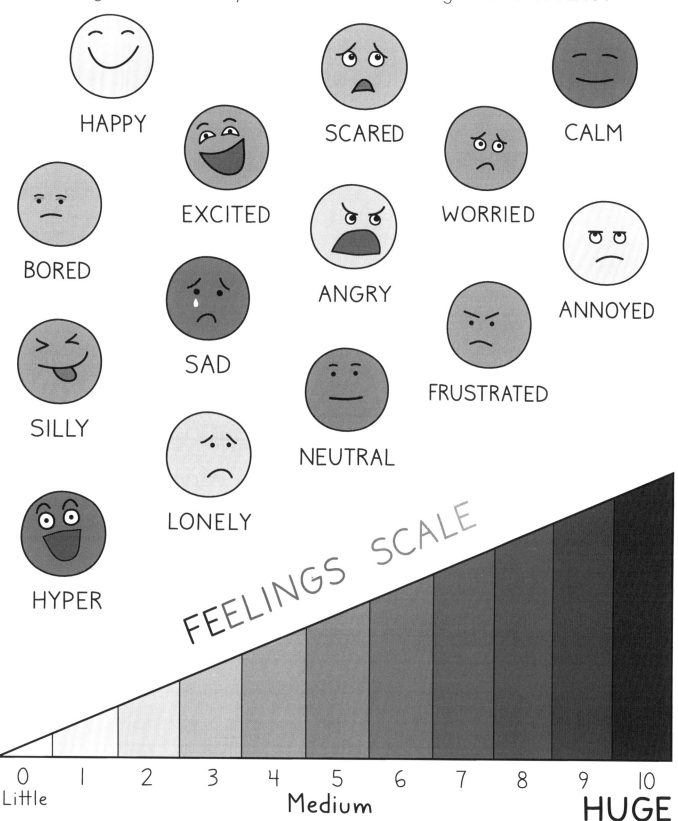

45

WHEN SOMEONE YOU LOVE HURTS YOU

When someone we care about hurts us, it's normal to have upset feelings towards that person and have loving feelings at the same time. You can have both; it's ok. Draw or write the upset feelings and the caring feelings you have towards the person who hurt you below.

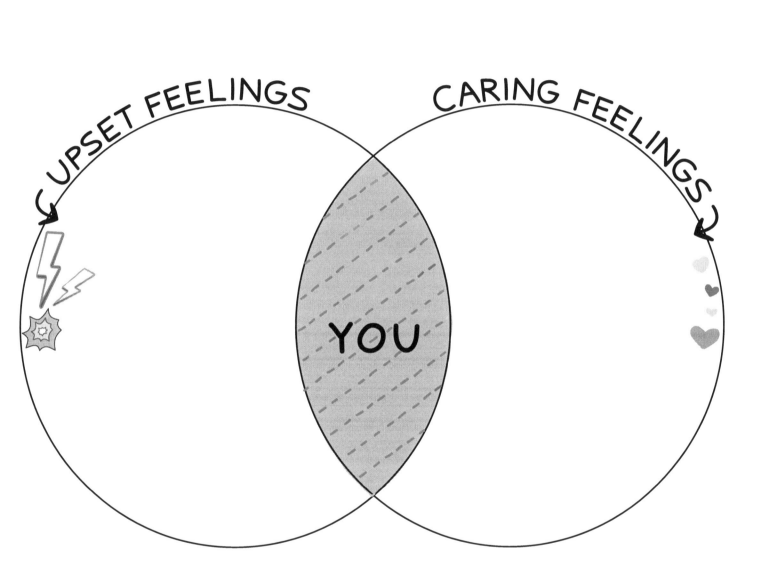

Brain & Thinking Reactions

FLASHBACKS

Kids who experience trauma can have unwanted memories, thoughts, images, or sensations of the trauma pop into their heads. These are called flashbacks and can be very upsetting. Draw or write the flashbacks you experience and practice changing the image below so you can use it in the future.

Draw/write your flashbacks here:

When this happens, circle what you will shout at them in your head

NO MEMORY!   NOT NOW!

GO AWAY!   DELETE!   OFF!

Now, fill your brain with something calm and kind to replace it with

I AM

Kids who have experienced a trauma sometimes have a hard time remembering all the good things about themselves. Circle the words below that are true for you. Add your own!

Blame Pie

When something bad happens kids often blame themselves, even if they did not really have control over the situation. In this blame pie, color in the section of blame each person involved has in what happened to you.

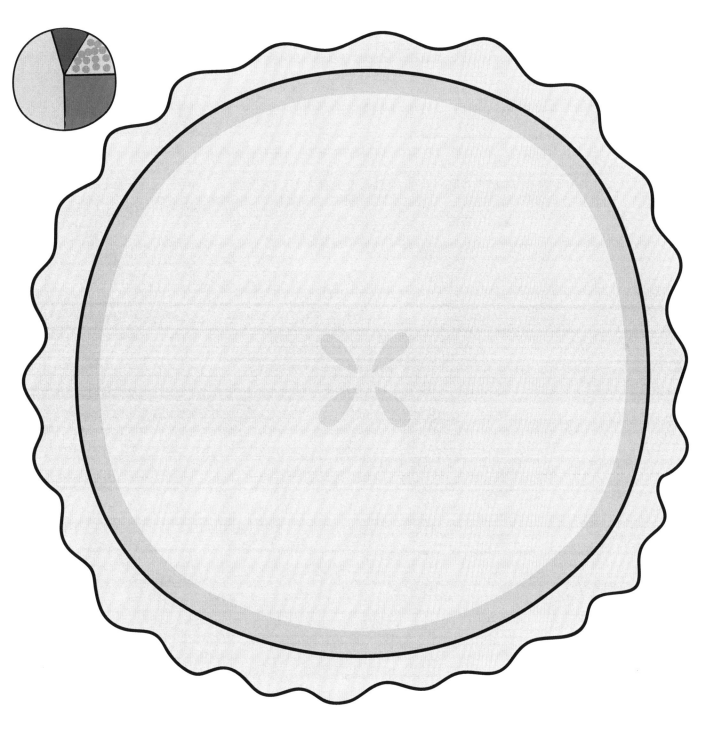

THERE IS SO MUCH MORE TO YOU THAN YOUR TRAUMA!

When a trauma happens, it can sometimes feel like that is all there is and all there will ever be. There is so much more to you and your life than what happened to you. Fill out each section below to celebrate the real you.

I like:

Food: Colors:

Music: Games:

Shows: Sports:

Movies: Celebrities:

Hobbies: Heroes:

I value (circle 3):

TRUST   SAFETY

HONESTY   LOVE

FAMILY   LOYALTY

FREEDOM   HELPING

RESPECT   MONEY

INTELLIGENCE   FAITH

HAPPINESS   PEACE

KINDNESS   STRENGTH

All About ME

What I'm good at:

I love:

My favorite people:

I am unique because:

I am lovable because:

CATCH YOUR THOUGHTS

Having a trauma can change the way we think about ourselves and about the world. Sometimes these thoughts are helpful, and other times the thoughts can make us feel bad or may not actually be true. Write down your thought below. With your therapist, take a closer look at that thought.

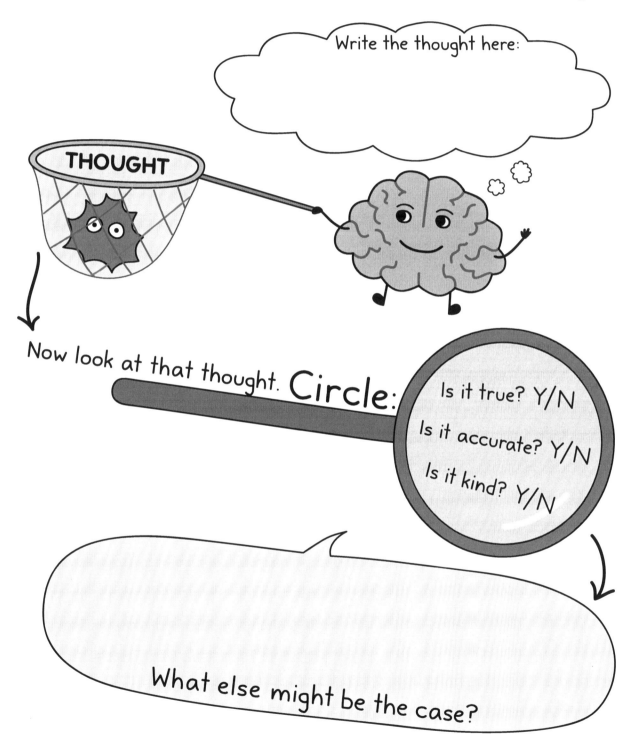

Write the thought here:

THOUGHT

Now look at that thought. Circle:

Is it true? Y/N

Is it accurate? Y/N

Is it kind? Y/N

What else might be the case?

WORRY BRAIN/SMART BRAIN

Worry is normal, all brains do it! Sometimes, worries get too big or get in the way of feeling calm and happy. Fill out the worries your Worry Brain has and write what Smart Brain might say back to it.

Meet Worry Brain!
He is trying to keep you safe by alerting you to possible dangers.

Meet Smart Brain!
He is a kind and wise friend to Worry Brain.

It's okay to feel that way! Here's what I think

I'm scared that _____

→

_____

I think about _____

→

_____

COLOR PAGE

Color in the I AM and then fill the paper with good things about yourself.
Take it home and put it where you can see it when you need a reminder.

CIRCLE OF TRUST

It can be hard to trust people after you have experienced a trauma. Write or draw the people who fit into your trust circle below.

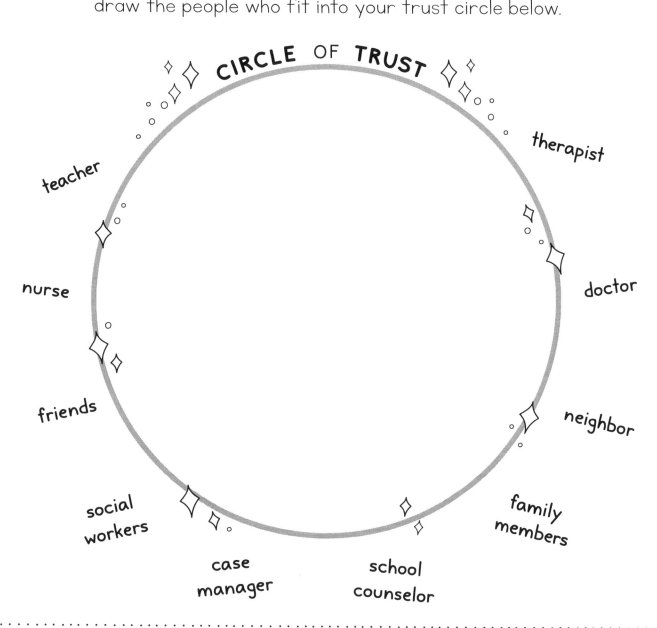

CIRCLE OF TRUST

- therapist
- doctor
- neighbor
- family members
- school counselor
- case manager
- social workers
- friends
- nurse
- teacher

How do these people show you they are safe and belong in this circle?

HIDDEN MEMORIES

Sometimes our brain hides parts of the stressful or traumatic event to help keep our feelings and behaviors safe. THANK YOU FOR TRYING TO PROTECT US BRAIN! When you are ready, your therapist can help you talk about and remember the details in a safe way. This might be through drawing or writing about what happened. If you want you can write a sentence or draw a picture about it here.

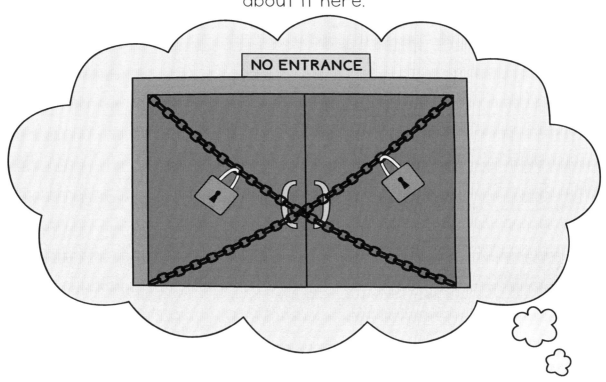

Are there any parts of your trauma your brain is trying squeeze away?

circle:

YES/NO

If you want you can write a sentence about it here

_____

LOYALTY CONFLICT

Sometimes kids experience something called a Loyalty Conflict. This happens when we feel stuck or caught between two people we care about. Loyalty Conflicts can feel really bad and bring up lots of upset feelings. One example is when we feel pressured to talk or think badly about someone we care about to make another person we care about happy. Write or draw the people you feel this is happening with. Then, write or draw how it feels and what you wish would happen.

PERSON A   YOU   PERSON B

How this feels (draw or write)

_____

_____

What I wish

_____

_____

ABOUT THE AUTHOR

Beth Richey is a Licensed Clinical Social Worker and Registered Play Therapist-Supervisor based in Philadelphia, PA. She is a creator of engaging, child-friendly therapeutic products and has multiple publications including: The Trauma Reaction Cards, Me Magnets, the Trauma Reminder & Coping Assessment Cards, Brain Mates, CBT Squishies, Mindset Magnets, Family Feelings, Me Messages, and Cognition Magnets. Find out more at www.BethRicheyCounseling.com

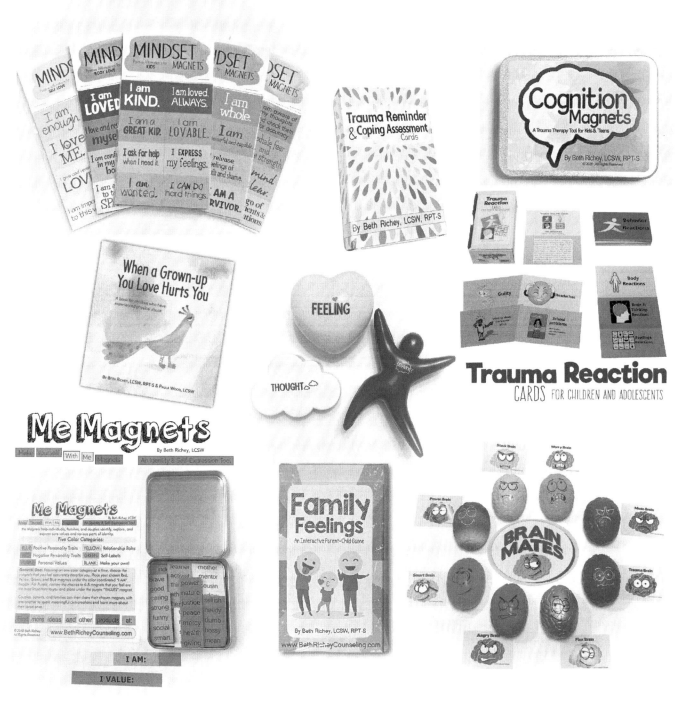

Made in the USA
Middletown, DE
05 December 2023

44775983R00064